Enjoying the Library

Book D

Written by Jane Price

Published by Prim-Ed Publishing

Enjoying the Library

A Library Skills Programme For Primary Schools
Book D

The *Enjoying The Library* series comprises six sequential packages, catering for all Year levels in the primary school. The packages are self-explanatory and have been designed for use in any library, regardless of the number of resources available to the pupils.

It should be stressed that the activities in the series are designed to be used by both classroom teachers and library specialists.

The series involves a thorough library programme. The emphasis is on 'hands-on' experience as this not only caters for individual abilities and differences but also gives pupils the opportunity to explore the resources available in the library.

The aim of this programme is to make students independent library users who can choose and use appropriate, relevant library resources. Specific reference to many parts of the shelves has been made to enable pupils to become familiar with the wide range of subjects offered.

Each package contains some forty activities lasting approximately thirty minutes each. This provides a complete year-long library study programme. However, in many schools a second period per week is also given. It is important that in the second session all pupils are given the opportunity to borrow resources. Lower primary pupils enjoy this time to be read a range of stories or be given the opportunity to complete any library work.

Suggestions for further research are given in the packages for the middle and upper primary Year levels. Appropriately, a research question relating to specific classroom activities should be given.

Contents

Caring for Books

Library books are precious, as not only are they enjoyable resources, but they cost money, and other people will also want to read them.

Below are a few simple suggestions to make sure books are cared for.

1. **Use a library bag.**

2. **Keep your books out of the sun and damp places.**

3. **No tearing, scribbling or spilling food onto your books.**

4. **Always put your books in a safe place where you can find them.**

5. **Always have clean hands before you begin to read.**

Revision
Library Quiz

Answer as many of these questions as you can.
Your teacher will go through the answers with you at the end of the lesson.

1. Write down the names of the people who work in the library.

   _____

2. Is the library open:

   Before School?   Yes/No

   Break?   Yes/No

   Lunchtime?   Yes/No

   After School?   Yes/No

3. How do you borrow a book?

   _____

   _____

   _____

4. How long can you borrow a book for?

   _____

5. Is fiction true or made-up?_____

6. Is non-fiction true or made-up?_____

7. How are fiction books arranged on the shelves?

   _____

8. How are non-fiction books arranged on the shelves?

   _____

9. Give an example of a reference book._____

10. How do you return your books?

    _____

    _____

Set up a plan of the library.

Cut out the sections of a library below and paste them on a piece of blank paper to make your own library plan.

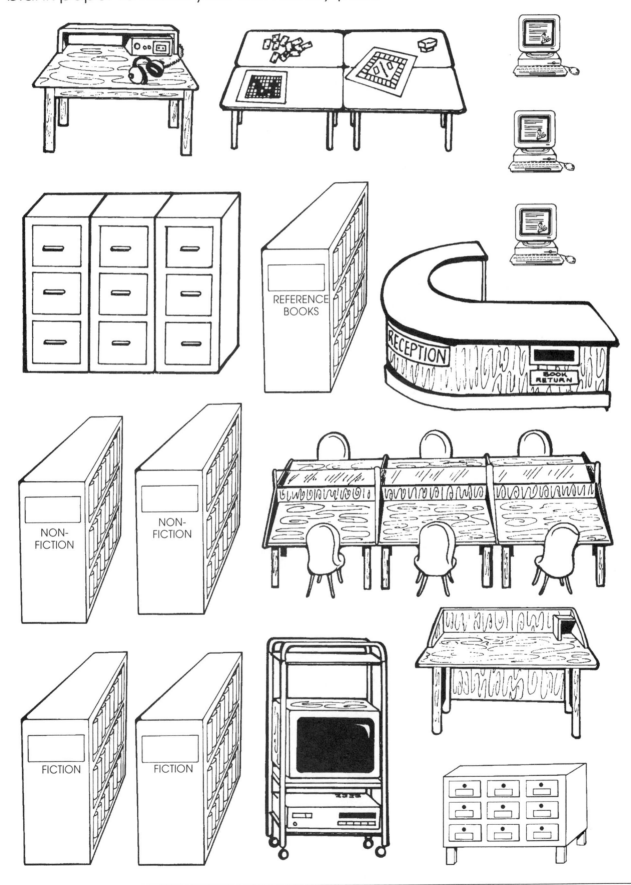

Areas in the Library

List the three main areas in the library.

F_____

N_____

R_____

Choose a book from each area.

Fill in the following blank spine labels.

F_____   N_____   R_____

Give two examples of a reference book. _____

_____

Can you borrow a reference book from the library?_____

Your teacher will give you two books. Write down the:

Title: _____

Author: _____

Illustrator: _____

Fiction/Non-fiction/Reference: _____

Title: _____

Author: _____

Illustrator: _____

Fiction/Non-fiction/Reference: _____

Fiction

What are fiction books?

_____

_____

How are they arranged on the fiction shelves?

_____

_____

_____

Put these authors' surnames into alphabetical order:

Spence   Townsend   Thiele   Dahl   Mahy
Martin   Blume   Jennings   Adams   Blyton

1._____   6._____

2._____   7._____

3._____   8._____

4._____   9._____

5._____   10._____

Using the card catalogue, computer (OPAC) or by browsing along the fiction shelves, locate and write the title of a book written by the following authors.

•Blume:_____

•Browne:_____

•Dahl:_____

•Jennings:_____

•Mahy:_____

Parts of a Fiction Book

Title

THE DAY MY PET TALKED

Spine
Label
(Call
Number)

F
LEE

Author

BY B. LEEVIT

Why is the spine label useful?

_____

_____

Choose a book from the shelf. From the book you have chosen,
draw and label the cover below.

Fiction Spine Label

Below is an example of a spine label. What do the letters on a spine label stand for?

F
PER

_____

_____

_____

_____

What would you find on the spine label of these books?

Smith	F
	SMI

Jones

Bone

Martin

Thomas

Browne

Cole

Reid

Gibbs

May

Put these in the order you would find them on the shelves.

1. _Bone_

2._____

3._____

4._____

5._____

6._____

7._____

8._____

9._____

10._____

Quick Revision:

The spine label of a fiction book contains the letter F which stands for
_____ and the first three letters of the Author's _____
(in most cases).

Locating Fiction Books (Non-automated Libraries)

You can find a fiction book if you know the T_____ or

A_____ of a book.

Sample of a catalogue card.

F BOW	Bowman, Kerry The Shot in the Night/ Kerry Bowman. - London: Publisher, 1989. 60p: ill (some col.),
ISBN	0-356-70117-0

Using the above catalogue card, write down the:

Author:_____

Title:_____

Call Number:

Using the catalogue, check to see if the library contains fiction books
with either the following titles or by the authors below:

Uncanny   Yes/No
Dahl, Roald   Yes/No
Moby Dick   Yes/No
Blyton, E   Yes/No
Winnie, the Pooh   Yes No

Choose two books in your library and complete the following:

Author: _____

Title: _____

Author: _____

Title: _____

Locating Fiction Books
(Automated Libraries)

Which searches on the computer terminals can you do to locate a fiction book?

_____   _____

_____   _____

AccⁿNo: 013976   Call Number: F BOW

No. copies: 1

Title: The Shot in the Night   Subject: Fiction

Author: Bowman, Kerry   Picture Book

Publisher: Penguin Place   Place Published: London

Date Published: 1989

Using the above information, write down the:

Author: _____

Title: _____

Call Number: [ ]

Using the computer terminals, check to see if the library holds the following titles of fiction books, or fiction books by the authors mentioned.

Uncanny	Yes/No
Dahl, Roald	Yes/No
Where the Forest Meets the Sea	Yes/No
Blyton, Enid	Yes/No
Superfudge	Yes/No

Fiction Title Card

Label the parts of the catalogue card.

```
The Shot in the Night
                                        _____

F        BOWMAN, Kerry  _____
BOW      The Shot in the Night/ Kerry
         Bowman. - London:
         Publisher, 1989. 60p:            _____
         ill (some col.),

ISBN     0-356-70117-0
```

_____

Using the above catalogue card, write down the:

Author_____

Title_____

Spine Label_____

If the following fiction books are available in the library, locate them
in the catalogue and write down their call number.

Superfudge   _____

ESIO Trot   _____

The Pinballs   _____

The Cat Ate my Gymsuit   _____

Willy the Wimp   _____

Your teacher may suggest additional Titles.

Fiction Title
(Automated Library)

When using the computer terminals to locate fiction titles, there are several methods you can use. The most common way is to do a _____ search. (You must know the exact title and spell it correctly.)

Can you do a title search if you:

(a)   only know part of the title?   Yes/No

(b)   know one or two words in the title?   Yes/No

(c)   know the author?   Yes/No

(d)   know the exact title?   Yes/No

Using the computer terminal, choose 'title search'. Locate one of the following titles:

Superfudge   The Cat Ate my Gymsuit

ESIO Trot   Willy the Wimp

Complete the following information from the computer screen.

Acc^N No:_____   Call Number:_____

Title:_____   Subject(s):_____

_____   _____

Author:_____   _____

Publisher:_____   Place Published:_____

Date Published:_____   ISBN:_____

Your teacher may suggest additional titles.

Fiction Book Review

Locate a fiction book you would like to read.

When you have finished reading it, answer this sheet.

Author:_____

Title:_____

Illustrator:_____

Spine Label:_____

Publisher:_____

Nasty characters:_____

_____

Nice characters:_____

_____

What was the story about?

_____

_____

_____

_____

_____

_____

_____

Did you like or dislike the story? Why/Why not?

_____

_____

_____

_____

_____

Fiction Quiz

1. What is fiction?_____

_____

_____

2. How are fiction books arranged on the shelf?_____

_____

3. What would you find on the spine labels of books by these authors?

Martin _____ Gretz _____

Dahl _____ Mahy _____

Briggs _____ Seuss _____

4. Write the spine labels in alphabetical order.

1. ☐   4. ☐

2. ☐   5. ☐

3. ☐   6. ☐

5. **Choose a fiction book.** Write down the:

Author:_____

Title:_____

Spine Label: ☐

Fiction Sleuth

R	E	A	S	D	R	A	C	E	U	G	O	L	A	T	A	C	D
I	N	G	I	S	F	U	N	Y	O	F	U	N	A	N	R	K	E
A	A	A	L	P	H	A	B	E	T	I	C	A	L	D	D	O	U
D	R	I	N	G	T	U	H	E	D	C	A	Y	A	N	D	O	B
V	E	M	F	E	L	T	I	T	O	T	R	E	Y	O	U	B	G
E	O	Y	T	O	S	H	L	S	P	I	N	E	L	A	B	E	L
N	E	S	L	E	V	O	N	E	P	O	A	T	N	I	G	R	H
T	T	T	E	V	E	R	R	Y	O	N	N	C	E	C	A	U	N
U	F	E	I	N	Y	R	O	T	S	T	R	O	H	S	D	T	A
R	G	R	R	E	A	T	B	O	O	K	I	M	N	T	H	C	E
E	L	Y	I	B	R	A	R	Y	H	A	V	I	E	S	O	I	M
N	O	I	T	C	I	F	E	C	N	E	I	C	S	E	E	P	N
C	H	A	R	A	C	T	E	R	S	J	O	S	Y	M	E	N	T

Find these words.

Adventure	Mystery
Alphabetical	Novel
Author	Picture Book
Catalogue Cards	Science fiction
Characters	Short Story
Comics	Spine Label
Fiction	Title

Write down the hidden message with the letters that are left.

_____

_____

_____

_____

Non-fiction

What are non-fiction books?_____

_____

_____

How are they arranged on the non-fiction shelves?

_____

_____

_____

_____

Write these numbers in order (as you would find them on the shelf).

| 623 | 592 | 400 | 001 | 920 | 262 |

1._____   4._____

2._____   5._____

3._____   6._____

Choose two non-fiction books from the shelves and complete the following:

Title: _____

Author(s): _____

Illustrator/Photographer: _____

_____

_____

Spine Label:

Dewey Decimal System

Melvil Dewey invented the Dewey Decimal System to make finding books on subjects easier. He divided all books into 10 main groups.

Fill in the different groups according to their numbers.

000 - 099 _____

100 - 199 _____

200 - 299 _____

300 - 399 _____

400 - 499 _____

500 - 599 _____

600 - 699 _____

700 - 799 _____

800 - 899 _____

900 - 999 _____

Although these are the main groups, each group is divided into more specialised fields.

Use a subject index to find out what subjects are found at:

808 _____

796 _____

001.64 _____

994 _____

523 _____

Parts of a Non-fiction Book

Match the following words with the correct part of the book. Draw lines to join the words to the features found on the cover of the book.

TITLE

SPINE LABEL
(CALL
NUMBER)

AUTHOR

727
SHE

BY
O. SHEN

D
O
L
P
H
I
N
S

Choose a non-fiction book from the shelf. Write down the:

Author: _____

Title: _____

Spine Label:

Describe the book you chose. Do you like it? Why/Why not?

_____

_____

_____

_____

_____

_____

Non-fiction Spine Label

736.7	Dewey Decimal Classification Number
KER	This is the number showing where the book will be found on the shelf.

736.7 — Dewey Decimal Classification Number
This is the number showing where the book will be found on the shelf.

KER — These are the first three letters of the author's surname.

Put the spine labels of the following books in order.

737 SMI	May
001 MAR	Thomas
900 COL	Bone
553 JON	Reid
331 THO	Martin

100 REI	Jones
800 MAY	Smith
420 BON	Colins
636 BRO	Gibbs
237 GIB	Brown

Table of Contents

1. The table of contents is found at the _____ of the book.

2. It is a list of _____ found inside the book.

3. It is not listed in _____ order, but in the order the chapters are found in the book.

Answer the following questions using the table of contents shown below.

1. How many chapters are there?_____

2. How long is the introduction?_____

3. On what page do we find information on 'Equipment'?_____

4. What chapter is 'Equipment'?_____

5. What do we find on page 117?_____

6. Which is the longest chapter?_____

7. What page is the index on?_____

The Index

1. Any index is an/a _____

   _____

2. It is usually found at the _____ of any non-fiction book, encyclopaedia, pamphlet etc.

   Answer the following questions using the index shown.

Index	
Bowling	5 - 33
-cricket	18 - 21
-indoor cricket	31 - 33
Equipment	45 - 79
-abseiling	53
-basketball	47 - 48, 50
-cricket	56, 58 - 62
-football	54 - 55
-hockey	62 - 63
-netball	45 - 47
Marking	76 - 96
-parks	76, 83
-courts	93 - 96
Rules	136 - 147
Uniforms	100 - 116
-boots	109 - 112
-colours	100 - 103
-shoes	103 - 109
-clothes	112 - 116

1. What do you find on the following pages?

   53 _____

   47 - 48, 50 _____

   62 - 63 _____

   100 - 116 _____

   5 - 33 _____

2. On what pages would you find the following subjects?

   Bowling - cricket _____

   Uniform - clothes _____

   Marking - parks _____

   Rules _____

   Equipment- netball _____

3. How many pages are used for each of the following subjects?

   Uniforms - shoes _____

   Equipment - cricket _____

   Bowling - indoor cricket _____

Decimals

Non-fiction books are arranged the shelves numerically. The books are given a decimal number according to their subject.

Try putting these numbers in order.

593.9	745.5	**001.64**
610	362.42	737.5
808.8	500	629.2
	994.94	

Example

1. **001.64**   2. _____   3. _____   4. _____

5. _____   6. _____   7. _____   8. _____

             9. _____   10. _____

Look through the non-fiction shelves in the library. What subjects do you find at these numbers?

001.64   _____

796   _____

500   _____

808.8   _____

994.94   _____

At what Dewey Decimal number would you find the following subjects:

Myths and Legends? _____   Birds? _____

Fashion? _____   Fairytales? _____

Investions? _____

Locating
Non-fiction Resources
(Non-automated Library)

Non-fiction books are arranged numerically according to their subject. Melvil Dewey devised these numbers. The numbers are known as the Dewey Decimal Classification System.

Subject Heading Index

The Subject Heading Index is a list of all subjects possibly found in a library. However, your library may not have all the subjects in the Subject Heading Index.

Using The Index

Like all indexes, the Subject Heading Index is arranged alphabetically. Try finding these subjects. Write the Dewey Decimal number next to the subject.

Prehistoric animals_____   Pop music_____

Space travel_____   Ducks_____

Koalas_____   Submarines_____

Football_____   English - History_____

Find these books on the shelves.

List a few of your favourite subjects and write the Dewey Decimal number next to the subject.

_____   _____

_____   _____

_____   _____

_____

Locating
Non-fiction Resources
(Automated Library)

Non-fiction books are arranged numerically according to their subject. Melvil Dewey devised these numbers. The numbers are known as the Dewey Decimal Classification System.

What searches can be done on the computer terminals to locate a non-fiction resource?

_____

_____

_____

_____

_____

Using the terminals, write the Dewey Decimal number next to the subjects below:

Prehistoric animals_____   Pop music_____

Space travel_____   Ducks_____

Rhinoceros _____   Submarines_____

Football_____   Gardening_____

Find these on the shelves.

List a few of your favourite subjects and write the Dewey Decimal number next to the subject.

_____   _____

_____   _____

_____   _____

Find the following books on the shelves.

What is the number given to these subjects?

Martial Arts_____

Health_____

Insects_____

Water Sports_____

Arms and Armour_____

Dinosaurs_____

Reptiles_____

Mythology_____

What subjects do we find at the following numbers? Use the front of the Subject Heading Index to help you.

370_____   400_____

160_____   570_____

510_____   700_____

780_____   220_____

340_____   690_____

Match the topics to the subject numbers.

Transport   595.7

Mammals   523

Solar System   629.2

Insects   537

Electricity   599

Subject Searches
(Automated)

Do a subject search on the computer terminal to find out if there is information in the library on the following topics. If there is nothing on the initial subject you have typed in, try another word for that subject.

For example -   *Prehistoric Animals*
                   alternate word
                   Dinosaurs

Martial Arts

alternate word

_____

Arms and Armour

alternate word

_____

Health

alternate word

_____

Reptiles

alternate word

_____

Insects

alternate word

_____

Aboriginal Mythology

alternate word

_____

Water Sports

alternate word

_____

Cooking

alternate word

_____

Find the non-fiction subject at the following numbers.

370 _____

160 _____

510 _____

780 _____

340 _____

700 _____

570 _____

700 _____

220 _____

690 _____

Using the Subject Heading Index 2

Match the following subjects with their Dewey Decimal numbers.

Calendars	634
Eye - Anatomy	553.3
Grapes	359
Housing	581
Iron	610.73
Plants	553.6
Computers	780
Nursing	509
Dolphins	529
Sand	001.64
Navy	306
Music	611
Water	629.2
Tyres	599.5
Scientists	553.7

Choose one of the above subjects:_____

Find a book on the shelf about that subject. Write down the:

Title:_____

Author:_____

Spine Label:

Using a
Non-fiction Book 1

Choose any one **Insect** to research.

What is the Dewey Decimal number of your topic? _____

Choose a book on your topic.

Write down the:

Author:_____

Title:_____

Call Number:_____

Write a short review on the book you have chosen.
Insect's body (camouflage, protection, movement)

_____

_____

_____

_____

Insect's home (location, materials)

_____

_____

_____

_____

Insect's life cycle

_____

_____

_____

_____

Locating Non-fiction Books Using the Catalogue

You can find a non-fiction book in the catalogue if you know the:

T _____ of the book.

A_____ of the book.

S _____ L _____ of the book.

Use the catalogue to find books for the following non-fiction subjects.

Ladybird _____

Flowering plants _____

Conservation (e.g. trees) _____

Choose a non-fiction book on a subject you are currently studying in class.

Fill in the blank catalogue card below with reference to the book you have chosen. (Include author, title, spine label etc.)

For example:

636.08

The Wideawake Mice

McCullagh,Sheila

Illus. by P. Theobalds

Ladybird Books Ltd, Loughborough

45p. Illus. 45

○

Does the book have an index?   Yes/No

Does the book have a contents page?   Yes/No

Does it have pictures?   Yes/No

Locating Non-fiction Books Using the Catalogue

Choose a non-fiction book.

If you could change the title of the book, what would you change it to and why?

_____

_____

_____

_____

Redesign the cover using your new title. (Include title and author.)

Locating Non-fiction Books in an Automated Library

You can find a non-fiction book using the computer terminal if you know the:

T _____ of the book.

A_____ of the book.

S _____ L _____ of the book

Choose a subject you are currently studying in class.

_____

Locate the Dewey Decimal number. _____

Find a book on this subject. Complete the following information:

Title _____

Author _____

Call Number _____

Does the book have an index?   Yes/No

Does the book have a contents page?   Yes/No

Does it have pictures?   Yes/No

How many pages does the book have?   _____

If you could change the title of the book, what would you change it to and why?

_____

_____

_____

_____

_____

Notemaking 1

Turtles

A turtle is a member of the reptile family as it is covered by scales or plates and it is cold-blooded and breathes air. The outstanding feature of the turtle is its hard shell. This shell can be up to a metre long and is made from rib bones covered with plates or scales.

The turtle cannot 'pull' its head inside its shell like a tortoise, which is a close relative. There are seven types of marine turtle in the world, but most live in the warm tropical oceans where they feed on algae and sea grasses.

Turtles will spend nearly all their life in the water, but the female will crawl out onto a beach to lay her rubbery-shelled eggs. The female digs a hole in the sand and lays up to two hundred eggs in it. The eggs are then covered with sand and hatch about eight weeks later. Unfortunately, most of the young turtles never survive their trip back to the water. They are easy prey for birds and other animals.

Underline the key words and phrases in the passage above.

Write your notes in the chart below. Remember to keep your notes brief.

Characteristics	How they live	Life cycle
• belongs reptile family • covered scales or plates		

Notemaking 1

Write a summary of the turtle passage. Start your summary by introducing the topic. The next three paragraphs should be a summary of the key points in the three sections of your chart. The last paragraph should be a comment to sum up the main points.

_____

_____

_____

_____

_____

_____

_____

_____

_____

_____

_____

_____

_____

_____

_____

_____

Draw a picture relating to your summary.

_____

_____

_____

_____

_____

Isle of Wight

The Isle of Wight is England's largest offshore island. The island has good beaches, facilities for fishing, and a long history of good sailing, making it a popular holiday resort. Tourism is a big part of the Isle's economy.

The Isle of Wight is located in the English Channel, opposite Hampshire on the south coast. The island is 37 kilometres long and nearly 21 kilometres wide. It has one of the warmest climates in England, averaging 5^{0}C in January and 17^{0}C in July. The annual rainfall is 760 millimetres.

The Isle of Wight has a long history. The most famous historic event occurred during the Civil War (1647) when King Charles I escaped to the island. He was kept under surveillance for over a year before being taken from the island and beheaded. The Isle of Wight also has many legends of shipwrecks and smuggling.

Subject: _____

Write notes in the space below.

Location	History	Holiday Island	Climate

Notemaking 2

Write a summary of the Isle of Wight passage.   Start your summary by introducing the topic. The next four paragraphs should be a summary of the key points in the four sections of your chart. The last paragraph should be a comment to sum up the main points.

_____

_____

_____

_____

_____

_____

_____

_____

_____

_____

_____

_____

_____

_____

_____

_____

_____

_____

_____

_____

_____

_____

Non-fiction Book Review

Choose any non-fiction book on the shelves.

Write down the following:

Author:_____

Title:_____

Call Number:_____

Write a summary of your book.

For Example :   Does it have pictures?
                 Is the information easy to understand?
                 Does it have an index and/or contents page?

_____

_____

_____

_____

_____

_____

_____

_____

_____

_____

_____

_____

Bibliography

Whenever you take information from another person's book, you need to write it down in the form of a bibliography to show you have used it.

Books:
   Author (Date), <u>Title of Book</u>, Publisher, City.

For example :
   Jones, R (1968), <u>The Play Book</u>, Macmillan, New York.

Reference Materials:
   Title of Article, (Year of Publication), Name of Reference Material, Publisher, City, Volume and Page Number(s).

   'Franc'(1991), The World Book Encyclopaedia, Hall Corp, Ontario, Vol 7 pp. 451.

Take two examples of non-fiction books and two examples of reference materials and write your own bibliography.

Non-fiction Books

1.

2.

Reference Materials
For example, Encyclopaedia.

1.

2.

Writing an Autobiography

An autobiography is a book which a person writes about himself or herself.

Write your autobiography on a separate sheet of paper. Use the following as a guide.

Likes

Interests

Friends

Address

Favourite places

Sports

Age

Family

Birthday

Pets

Dislikes

Hospital born in

School

Ambitions

Name

Non-fiction Quiz

What is a non-fiction book?_____

_____

What do you find on a non fiction spine label? _____

_____

_____

Under what Dewey Decimal numbers would you find the following subjects?

Noise_____ Sun_____

Jokes, English_____ Origami_____

Gymnastics_____ Folklore_____

Costumes_____ Lions_____

Organise the above into the order you would find them on the shelf.

(a)_____ (e)_____

(b)_____ (f)_____

(c)_____ (g)_____

(d)_____ (h)_____

Choose a non-fiction book. Locate the:

Author_____

Title_____

Call Number_____

Non-fiction Sleuth

K	Y	O	S	O	C	I	A	L	S	C	I	E	N	C	E	S	N
A	H	H	N	I	V	A	P	O	S	N	M	I	S	T	O	K	L
R	P	S	A	O	R	T	C	U	U	L	M	O	P	A	F	C	A
T	A	P	W	R	N	Y	I	N	B	B	L	R	I	B	E	O	M
A	R	S	T	I	U	F	N	G	J	N	R	F	N	L	O	M	I
N	G	R	S	M	M	A	I	T	E	I	W	N	E	E	Y	P	C
D	O	T	C	U	E	C	A	C	C	A	T	A	L	O	G	U	E
L	I	C	I	N	R	F	E	L	T	I	T	I	A	F	N	T	D
I	B	A	E	D	I	L	R	Y	H	I	I	N	B	C	F	E	Y
T	O	L	N	P	C	R	M	S	E	A	O	T	E	O	I	R	E
E	T	L	C	R	A	N	Y	E	A	O	U	N	L	N	W	T	W
R	U	N	E	A	L	N	T	H	D	A	N	D	A	T	H	E	E
A	A	U	T	H	O	R	U	C	I	L	M	N	O	E	P	R	D
T	R	M	T	U	R	A	C	R	N	L	A	P	S	N	A	M	S
U	S	B	I	G	D	N	M	A	G	E	O	T	O	T	T	I	F
R	O	E	R	Y	E	O	U	E	I	N	D	E	X	S	R	N	O
E	W	R	N	E	R	N	T	S	N	E	R	E	S	T	N	A	O
W	Y	K	D	F	E	B	M	W	D	N	M	O	Q	R	F	L	A
V	O	B	O	O	K	C	O	V	E	R	U	R	S	B	L	N	O
N	J	I	X	G	I	N	N	B	X	F	O	P	E	K	T	P	T

Find the following words:

Art and Literature
Author
Autobiography
Book Cover
Call Number
Catalogue

Computer Terminal
Dewey Decimal
Index
Numerical Order
Non-fiction
Science

Searches
Social Sciences
Spine Label
Subject Heading Index
Table of Contents
Title

Reference Material

Have you used the following? Tick the box.

Encyclopaedias ☐

Dictionaries ☐

Atlases ☐

DICTIONARY

WORLD BOOK

Locate the reference shelf in your library.

Are all reference books found in one place?_____

List some of the reference books found in the library.

_____   _____

_____   _____

_____   _____

_____   _____

Why can't you borrow reference materials?

_____

_____

_____

Draw the cover of a reference book.

How is this different from fiction/non-fiction books?

_____

_____

_____

_____

_____

_____

Encyclopaedias

List five sets of encyclopaedias you have in your library.

(a)_____

(b)_____

(c)_____

(d)_____

(e)_____

Which set of encyclopaedias do you use the most?

_____

Why do you use these?

_____

Choose any subject in the encyclopaedia.

Subject chosen_____

Encyclopaedia_____

Page and Volume_____
How much information is given on the subject?
(Number of paragraphs/pages. Are there pictures?)

_____

_____

_____

Write a short paragraph explaining the subject you chose.

_____

_____

_____

_____

Using Indexes
for Encyclopaedias

Most sets of encyclopaedias have an index. In many cases, the index is at the back of the last volume in the set. Some include a separate book with the index in it. Can you find the indexes to the encyclopaedias in your library?

Example:

Fur F: 487 (with pictures).		Fuse (electricity)	F: 511
Camel	C: 65	Electric circuit	E: 122
Clothing	Ci: 554	Electric wiring	E: 145
Hair H: 9			
Fur Seal		Fusion Jazz	
Alaska	A: 283	Jazz	J: 56
Antarctica	A: 498	Pop Music	P: 596
Furniture	T: 495 (with pictures)	Futures (economics)	
Folk Art	F: 280	Cotton	Ci: 871
Lacquer	L: 25	Wheat	W: 227-228

Using the above index, give the volume and page number of the subjects below.

Fur_____   Fuse_____

Camel_____   Electric circuit_____

Hair_____   Fusion Jazz_____

Fur Seal - Antarctica_____   Pop Music_____

Furniture_____   Futures Cotton_____

Lacquer_____   Wheat_____

Using Encyclopaedias 1

Choose a sport which interests you:_____

Write down:

Encyclopaedia Title:_____

Volume Number:_____

Page Number:_____

(Always write this down so you can find the information quickly if you need to go back to it.)

Write some notes on each of the following.

History	
Equipment and Uniform	
Rules	

Using Encyclopaedias 2

List four countries you can think of.
Underneath each country, write down an encyclopaedia which contains information on it.

1._____   2._____

_____   _____

3._____   4._____

_____   _____

Choose one country. Write notes on the following:

Geography	Way of Life	History	Climate	Extra Information
e.g. Where is it? Famous landforms. Population	e.g. Food Religion Education Housing Dress Recreation		Does it snow? Does it rain?	e.g. Currency

Using Encyclopaedias 3

For this activity use an encyclopaedia you don't normally use.

Choose any topic which interests you:_____

Locate the information in the encyclopaedia.

    Encyclopaedia's name:_____

    Volume Number:_____

    Page Number:_____

Look carefully at the information given on your topic. Decide on three areas you want to find out more about. These are called subheadings.

Write them below:

Subheading	
Subheading	
Subheading	
Subheading	

Dictionaries

Use these words to fill in the paragraph below.

first   **meaning**   **spelling**   **alphabetically**

Dictionaries give the **m**_____ of words. You find a
word in the dictionary by looking under the **f**_____
letter, as dictionaries are arranged **a**_____. They also
help you with the **s**_____ of a particular word.

Put these words into the order you would find them in the dictionary.

Emotion   (a)_____

Wrap   (b)_____

Basket   (c)_____

Desk   (d)_____

Liquid   (e)_____

Maximum   (f)_____

Rule   (g)_____

Smooth   (h)_____

Fright   (i)_____

Natural   (j)_____

List some of the dictionaries in your library.

(a)_____   (c)_____

(b)_____   (d)_____

Using Dictionaries 1

Write the dictionary meanings of the following words, then write your own meaning.

(a) Weight: _____

_____

(b) Entertain: _____

_____

(c) Heat: _____

_____

(d) Oxygen: _____

_____

(e) Animal: _____

_____

(f) Wheat: _____

_____

(g) Sport: _____

_____

Put the above words into alphabetical order.

(a)_____   (b)_____   (c)_____

(d)_____   (e)_____   (f)_____

(g)_____

Using Dictionaries 2

Define the following words using your own words.

Disguise:_____

_____

Improper:_____

_____

Peal:_____

_____

Game:_____

_____

Emotion:_____

_____

Put the above words into sentences.

(a) _____

_____

(b) _____

_____

(c) _____

_____

(d) _____

_____

(e) _____

_____

Atlases

Atlases show us where different places in the world are located.

They also give information on population, natural resources, agriculture and climate.

Look through an atlas.

Can you find these places? (Tick the box when you find it.)

Page No.

Australia _____

Africa _____

France _____

Greece _____

Papua New Guinea _____

China _____

Singapore _____

Scotland _____

Switzerland _____

The town in which you live. _____

Locate the * Index _____

              * Contents page _____

              * Key _____

Have a look through the atlas. Find the maps which show where natural resources are found (e.g. minerals - gold, coal etc).

Choose one of the above-mentioned coutries and write down its natural resources.

_____

_____

_____

Using the Atlas Index

Sample of atlas index below.

	Page	Ref.	Lat.	Long.
Gibson Desert	47	Dd	27 S	126 E
Great Barrier Reef	19	Dd	19 S	149 E
Greece	48	Ac	31 S	115 E
Grenada	41	Ki	12 N	61 W
Goa		Gg	15 N	73 E
Gold Coast	20	Ge	28	153
Germany - West	122	Fd	52 N	90 E
Great Wall	23	Ed	38 N	109 E
Honduras	16	Fc	14 N	86 W
Helsinki	48	Ce	42 S	147 S
Hawaii	56	Ji	20 N	157 W
Hiroshima	72	Fe	34 N	132 E
Hong Kong	77	Ib	22 N	114 E

Answer the following questions.

1. What page will you find these places on?

Great Wall _____   Helsinki _____

Gold Coast _____   Hong Kong _____

Greece _____   Gibson _____

Germany - West _____   Goa _____

Great Barrier Reef _____   Hawaii _____

2. Give the coordinates for the following places.

	Reference	Latitude	Longitude
Hiroshima	_____	_____	_____
Grenada	_____	_____	_____
Gold Coast	_____	_____	_____
Gibson Desert	_____	_____	_____
Honduras	_____	_____	_____

Using the Atlas 1

Place these towns and cities onto the map of Australia and then write down the nearest grid references.

* Brisbane_____

* Cairns_____

* Meekatharra _____

* Tennant Creek _____

* Perth _____

* Carnarvon _____

* Darwin _____

* Hobart _____

Using the Atlas 2

Place these towns and cities onto the map of the United Kingdom and then write down the nearest grid references.

* Birmingham_____

* London _____

* Manchester _____

* Liverpool _____

* Sheffield _____

* Bristol _____

* Isle of Wight _____

* Portsmouth _____

* Glasgow _____

Vertical File

Locate the vertical file in your library.

What type of information is kept in the vertical file?

_____

_____

_____

List five topics in the vertical file.

1. _____

2. _____

3. _____

4. _____

5. _____

Choose one of the above topics.

(a) List what information is in the file, e.g. newspaper clippings.

_____   _____

_____   _____

(b) Using the information available, write a summary of the topic you chose.

_____

_____

_____

_____

_____

_____

_____

_____

Reference Quiz

What is a reference book?_____

_____

_____

Give three examples of reference books you have used.

　　1.　　_____

　　2.　　_____

　　3.　　_____

Explain how to use:

(a) an encyclopaedia index:_____

_____

(b) a dictionary:_____

_____

(c) an atlas:_____

_____

Choose an animal you like:_____

Find the animal in an encyclopaedia and complete the questions below:

　　Name of the encyclopaedia_____

　　Volume Number_____

　　Page Number_____

Where is your animal found?_____

Can it be a pet?_____

What does it eat?_____

Is there a lot of these animals?_____

How long do they usually usually live for?_____

Reference Sleuth

N	R	E	M	E	A	N	I	N	G	R	P	M	F	S	L	R	R
O	E	E	N	N	C	E	M	A	X	E	D	N	I	T	O	E	R
I	F	I	A	C	L	P	Q	S	E	F	N	O	T	C	N	A	L
T	E	O	B	Y	E	B	H	E	R	E	O	T	E	E	G	D	A
A	R	D	I	C	T	I	O	N	A	R	Y	H	I	J	I	Y	C
M	E	F	R	L	K	I	V	M	T	E	H	E	R	B	T	R	I
R	N	R	Y	O	O	E	E	E	A	N	P	S	C	U	U	E	T
O	C	M	E	P	O	A	R	D	E	C	R	A	A	S	D	F	E
F	E	N	O	A	B	Q	V	U	I	E	C	U	R	F	E	E	B
N	S	F	E	E	D	E	I	T	C	B	E	R	O	O	O	R	A
I	K	S	T	D	L	I	E	I	V	O	L	U	M	E	S	E	H
L	C	M	T	I	R	E	W	T	N	O	S	S	H	G	E	N	P
S	A	L	T	A	O	E	I	A	T	K	H	E	L	N	I	C	L
J	X	A	Q	Y	W	T	A	L	L	S	T	I	S	A	L	E	A
D	E	F	I	N	I	T	I	O	N	S	M	E	S	R	S	O	P

Find these words in the sleuth:

Alphabetical
Atlas
Definitions
Dictionary
Encyclopaedia
Index
Information
Longitude
Latitude

Meaning
Overview
Ready Reference
Reference Books
References
Range of Subjects
Thesaurus
Volume
World Book

Bingo

Requirements
One card per student
Counters
Word cards (for bingo caller)

What to do:
Students are given a card. The Bingo caller chooses a word and calls it out clearly. The first person to cover all the words on his or her card with the counters calls 'Bingo' and is the winner.

Atlas	Index	Author
Library	Catalogue	Non-fiction
Dewey Decimal	Contents Page	Computers
Reference	Dictionary	Spine Label
Fiction	Title	Encyclopaedia

Bingo

library	non-fiction	reference
computers	author	Dewey decimal
contents page	catalogue	title

library	fiction	non-fiction
reference	computers	atlas
catalogue	author	dictionary

Dewey decimal	contents page	index
fiction	non-fiction	computers
dictionary	reference	author

library	author	Dewey decimal
computers	fiction	non-fiction
spine label	title	index

author	computers	catalogue
index	reference	fiction
non-fiction	title	library

encyclopaedia	index	library
spine label	author	computers
fiction	non-fiction	reference

computers	author	atlas
Dewey decimal	title	encyclopaedia
index	fiction	non-fiction

index	catalogue	Dewey decimal
encyclopaedia	spine label	library
title	atlas	fiction

non-fiction	reference	spine label
atlas	index	title
dictionary	contents page	Dewey decimal

library	spine label	fiction
non-fiction	reference	index
catalogue	atlas	title

bri

Research 1

Resources needed to carry out the lessons in this package are:

Fiction book collection
Non-fiction book collection
Subject Heading Index
Encyclopaedias
Dictionary
Atlas

Read the question and highlight/underline key words to help you locate the specific research material in your library.

Research Questions

1. Name the planets of the solar system. List the planets' individual features. How are they different from each other?

2. You are being sent to a planet. Which planet would you go to and why? Consider - temperature, gravity etc.

3. What are the four seasons? List the features of each. What happens to the length of day and night in these seasons?

4. Do seasons affect plants, animals or people? If so, how do they affect them?

5. What are some of the main features of the natural environment of a desert?

6. What are 'values'? Why are they important to you? What are some values of our culture?

7. Who was Christopher Columbus? Why was he famous?

8. Choose an explorer. Give details of his or her life.

9. Who were some of the earliest Europeans to visit Australia?

10. How would you describe a 'family'? What is an 'extended family'?

11. Define the following words:

* angles
* surface
* shape
* balance
* volume

* shapes
* classification
* symmetry
* scale

12. A windmill has a 'full-turn', scissors have a 'half-turn'. What is meant by these terms?

13. What are some measurements of length and distance? When is each used? Do different countries use different methods of measurement?

14. What are the months of the year? What do they mean?

15. Where did our system of numbers come from?

16. What is the difference between a solid, liquid and gas?

17. What is the ozone layer? What is happening to it?

18. What is the difference between natural and human-made environments?

19. How do plants grow? What conditions do they need?

20. Explain 'temperature'.